DR

Stage&Screen

**Exclusive Distributors
Music Sales Limited
8/9 Frith Street,
London W1V 5TZ, England.
Music Sales Pty Limited
120 Rothschild Avenue,
Rosebery, NSW 2018,
Australia.**

**Order No. AM92248
ISBN 0-7119-4373-7**
This book © Copyright 1995 by Wise Publications

**Book design by Pearce Marchbank, Studio Twenty
Cover illustration by Mark Thomas
Music compiled by Peter Evans**

**Printed in the United Kingdom by
Redwood Books Limited, Trowbridge, Wiltshire.**

**Your Guarantee of Quality
As publishers, we strive to produce every book to the
highest commercial standards.
This book has been carefully designed to minimise awkward
page turns and to make playing from it a real pleasure.
Particular care has been given to specifying acid-free,
neutral-sized paper made from pulps which have not been
elemental chlorine bleached.
This pulp is from farmed sustainable forests and was
produced with special regard for the environment.
Throughout, the printing and binding have been planned to
ensure a sturdy, attractive publication which should
give years of enjoyment.
If your copy fails to meet our high standards,
please inform us and we will gladly replace it.**

Music Sales' complete catalogue describes thousands of
titles and is available in full colour sections by subject, direct
from Music Sales Limited. Please state your areas of interest
and send a cheque/postal order for £1.50 for postage to:
Music Sales Limited, Newmarket Road,
Bury St. Edmunds, Suffolk IP33 3YB.

**Wise Publications
London/New York/Paris/Sydney/Copenhagen/Madrid**

12.95

Food Glorious Food

Words & Music by Lionel Bart

Where Is Love

Words & Music by Lionel Bart

Slowly, but rhythmically

Where ___ Is Love? Does it fall from skies a - bove?

Is it un-der-neath the wil-low tree ___ that I've been dream-ing of?

Where ___ is she who I close my eyes to see? Will I ev - er know the

Pick A Pocket Or Two

Words & Music by Lionel Bart

VERSE

1. In this life one thing counts: In the bank large a - mounts!
2. Why should we break our backs, Stup - id - ly pay - ing tax?
3. Rob - in Hood, what a crook! Gave a - way what he took,
4. Take a tip from Bill Sikes: He can whip what he likes,

I'm a - fraid these don't grow on trees, You've got to Pick A Pock - et Or Two.
Bet - ter get some un - taxed in - come:___ Bet - ter Pick A Pock - et Or Two.
Char - i - ty's fine, sub - scribe to mine, Get out and Pick A Pock - et Or Two.
I re - call he start - ed small, He had to Pick A Pock - et Or Two. You've

CHORUS

got to Pick A Pock - et Or Two, Boys, you've got to Pick A Pock - et Or Two!

Consider Yourself

Words & Music by Lionel Bart

don't want to have ___ no fuss ___ For aft - er some con-

sid - er - a - tion, we can state: Con - sid - er Your - self ___ one of

us. Con - sid - er Your - self ___

one of us. ___

13

I'd Do Anything

Words & Music by Lionel Bart

Anniversary Song

Words & Music by Al Jolson & Saul Chaplin

-cept _____ for the few _____ that were there _____ in your
find _____ that our love _____ is un - al - tered by

To next strain | *Fine*

eyes. time. _____ Dear, as I held you so close in my

arms, An-gels were sing-ing a hymn to your charms Two hearts gent-ly

beat-ing were mur-mur-ing low "My dar-ling, I love you so." _____ The

D.S. 𝄋 al Fine

Cabaret

Music by John Kander
Lyrics by Fred Ebb

Maybe This Time

Music by John Kander
Lyrics by Fred Ebb

Mein Herr

Music by John Kander
Lyrics by Fred Ebb

Bye bye mein lie - ber Herr.___ Auf wie - der - sehen, Mein Herr.___ Es war sehr
lie - ber Herr.___ Fare - well, mein lie - ber Herr.___ It was a

gut, Mein Herr,___ und vor - bei.___ Du kennst mich
fine af - fair,___ but now it's o - ver.___ And though I

wohl, Mein Herr.___ Ach, le - be wohl, Mein Herr.___ Du sollst mich
used to care,___ I need the o - pen air.___ You're bet - ter

nie mehr se - hen, Mein Herr Bye, bye mein

Coda

off with-out ____ me, You'll get on with-out me, Mein

(very fast)

Herr. ____

Money, Money

Music by John Kander
Words by Fred Ebb

buck or a pound

buck or a pound is all that makes the world go a-round, that clink-ing, clank-ing

Fm   Bb11

Gm   G7   C   C

sound can make the world go round. *Both:* Mon-ey, mon-ey, mon-ey, mon-ey,

Girl: Mon-ey, mon-ey, mon-ey, mon-ey, mon-ey, mon-ey, mon-ey, mon-ey,

Cm   G7

mon-ey, mon-ey, mon-ey, mon-ey, mon-ey, mon-ey, mon-ey, mon-ey. *Boy:* If you hap-pen to be rich, and you feel like a

Cm   G7

mon-ey, mon-ey, mon-ey, mon-ey, mon-ey, mon-ey, mon-ey, mon-ey, mon-ey, mon-ey, mon-ey, mon-ey, mon-ey, mon-ey, mon-ey, mon-ey,

night's en-ter-tain-ment, you can pay for a gay es-ca-pade. If you hap-pen to be rich, and a-lone, and you

Hello Dolly

Words & Music by Jerry Herman

From Russia With Love

Words & Music by Lionel Bart

Blue Suede Shoes

Words & Music by Carl Lee Perkins

Can't Help Falling In Love

Words & Music by George Weiss, Hugo Peretti & Luigi Creatore

Jailhouse Rock

Words & Music by Jerry Leiber & Mike Stoller

Medium Bright Rock

1. The

CHORUS

1. war-den threw a par-ty in the coun-ty jail._ The pri-son band was there and they be-
2. Spi-der Mur-phy play'd the ten-or sax-o-phone._ Lit-tle Joe was blow-in' on the
3. Num-ber For-ty-sev-en said to Num-ber Three_ "You're the cut-est jail-bird I

F (Tacet)   E   F (Tacet)

-gan to wail._ The band was jump-in' and the joint be-gan to swing._ You
slide trom-bone._ The drum-mer boy from Il-li-nois went crash, boom, bang!_ The
ev-er did see._ I sure would be de-light-ed with your com-pa-ny.__ Come

E   F (Tacet)   E

EXTRA CHORUSES

4. The sad sack was a-sittin' on a block of stone,
    Way over in the corner weeping all alone.
    The warden said, "Hey buddy, don't you be no square,
    If you can't find a partner, use a wooden chair!"
    Let's rock, etc.

5. Shifty Henry said to Bugs, "For Heaven's sake,
    No one s lookin', now's our chance to make a break."
    Bugsy turned to Shifty and he said, "Nix, nix,
    I wanna stick around a while and get my kicks,"
    Let's rock, etc.

Love Me Tender

Words & Music by Elvis Presley & Vera Matson

life   com - plete,   And   I   love   you   so.
I   be - long,   And   we'll   nev - er   part.
all   the   years,   Till   the   end   of   time.
fol - low   you   Ev - 'ry - where   you   go

CHORUS

Love me ten - der,   love me true,   All my dreams ful -

-fill   For, my dar - lin', I love you,

And I al - ways will.   And I al - ways will.

Return To Sender

Words & Music by Otis Blackwell & Winfield Scott

Moderately

Chorus

I gave a let-ter to the post-man; he put it in his sack.
So then I dropped it in the mail-box and sent it Spe-cial D.

Bright and ear-ly next morn-ing he brought my let-ter back.
Bright and ear-ly next morn-ing it came right back to me.

She wrote up-on it: Re-turn to send-er,

Aquarius

Words by James Rado & Gerome Ragni
Music by Galt MacDermot

Harmony and understanding, Sympathy and trust abounding.

No more falsehoods or derisions, Golden living dreams of visions, Mystic crystal revelation, And the mind's true liberation. Aquarius, Aquarius. When the

D.S. al Fine

51

Hair

Words by James Rado & Gerome Ragni
Music by Galt MacDermot

54

ga ga at the go go when they see me in my to - ga, My

to - ga made of blond, bril - liant - ined, bib - li - cal hair. My hair like Je - sus wore it, Hal - le -

lu - jah, I a - dore it, Hal - le - lu - jah; Mar - y loved her son, why don't my moth - er love me?

Hair, hair, hair, hair, hair, hair, hair, hair. Flow it, show it, long__ as God can grow it, my__

Hair   Flow it,   Show it,   long__ as God can grow it, my__
Hair   Flow it,   Show it,   long__ as God can grow it, my__ Hair.

Easy to Be Hard

Words by James Rado & Gerome Ragni
Music by Galt MacDermot

Good Morning Starshine

Words by James Rado & Gerome Ragni
Music by Galt MacDermot

Let The Sunshine In

Words by James Rado & Gerome Ragni
Music by Galt MacDermot

preme vi-sions of lone-ly tunes. Some-where, in-side some-thing, there is a rush of great-ness. Who knows what stands in front of our lives; I fash-ion my__ fu-ture on films in space. Si-lence tells me se-cret-ly ev-'ry-thing,_____ ev-'ry-thing.__

Company

Music & Lyrics by Stephen Sondheim

Being Alive

Music & Lyrics by Stephen Sondheim

Someone Is Waiting

Words & Music by Stephen Sondheim

Ain't Misbehavin'

Words by Andy Razaf
Music by Thomas Waller & Harry Brooks

My love was giv- en, heart and soul,___ So it can stand the test.
And made you mine a - lone for keeps,___ Dit - to to all you say.

Moderately (♫ = ♩³♪)

Chorus:

No one to talk with, all by my - self, No one to walk with, but

I'm hap - py on ___ the shelf, Ain't Mis - be - hav - in',

I'm sav - in' my love for

you. ___ I know for cer - tain

How Ya Baby

Words by J C Johnson
Music by Thomas Waller

78

kill - er - dill - er with noth - in' on___ my___ mind.

When they start to play - in' sweet songs,___ it

leaves me on the rocks,___ When they start to play - in'

sweet songs,___ it beats me to my socks.___ *(Spoken:) How Ya*

I Can't Give You Anything But Love

Words by Dorothy Fields
Music by Jimmy McHugh

The Joint Is Jumpin'

Words by Andy Razaf & J.C. Johnson
Music by Thomas Waller

They have a new ex - pres - sion a - long old Har - lem way____ that tells you when a par - ty is ten times more____ than gay.____ To say that things are jump - in' leaves not a sin - gle doubt ____ that

This here spot_ is more than hot,_ in fact the joint is jump - in'.
Grab a jug_ and cut the rug, _ I mean this joint is jump - in'.

Check your weap - ons at the door,_ be sure to pay your quar - ter.
Get your pig feet, beer and gin, _ there's plen - ty in the kitch - en.

Burn your leath - er on the floor,_ grab an - y - bod - y's daugh - ter.
Who is that that just came in?_ Just look at the way he's switch - in'.

The roof is rock - in', the neigh-bor's knock - in'.
Don't mind the hour, _____ 'cause I'm in pow - er.

86

Secret Love

Words by Paul Francis Webster
Music by Sammy Fain

REFRAIN: Moderately, *with much tenderness*

89

The Deadwood Stage (Whip-Crack-Away)

Words by Paul Francis Webster
Music by Sammy Fain

Dead-wood Stage is a-head-in' on o-ver the hills, _____ where the In-jun ar-rows are a-thick-er than por-ker-pine quills, _____ Dan-ger-ous land _____ no time to-de-lay, _____

Whip-crack-a-way, whip-crack-a-way, whip-crack-a-way. _____ We're head-in' straight for town, turn-in' round,

load-ed down with a fan-cy car-go, Care of Wells and Far-go, Ill-i-nois. Boy! Oh, The

homeward bound, can't cha hear 'em hum-min'! Hap-py times a-com-in' fer to stay, Hey! We'll be

Dead-wood Stage is a - com-in' on o - ver the crest, ____ Like a hom - in' pig - eon that's a -
home to night by the light of the sil-ver-y moon, ____ And my heart's a thump-in' like a

-hank-er-in' af-ter its nest, ____ Twen-ty three miles ____ to cov-er to-day, _
man-do-lin plunk-in' a tune, ____ When I get home ____ I'm fix-in' ter stay, _

So Whip-crack-a-way, whip-crack-a-way, whip-crack a - way. ____ The wheels go - way. ____
So Whip-crack-a-way, whip-crack-a-way, whip-crack-a -

Whip-crack-a-way, whip-crack-a-way, whip-crack a - way! ____

An Apple For The Teacher

Words by Johnny Burke
Music by James V. Monaco

Little Tin Box

Music by Jerry Bock
Lyrics by Sheldon Harnick

pos - i - tive your hon - or must be jok - ing,___ An - y
ply - ing I'm a crook and I say no sir ___ There is
see your hon - or does - n't pull his punch - es___ *And it*

work - ing man could do what I have done For a
noth - ing in my past I care to hide I've been
looks a tri - fle fish - ey I'll ad - mit *But for*

month or two I sim - ply gave up smok - ing___ And I
tak - ing emp - ty bot - tles to the gro - cer___ And each
one whole week I went with - out my lunch - es___ *And it*

put my ex - tra pen - nies one by one)
nick - el that I got was put a - side} in - to a
mount - ed up your hon - or bit by bit)

Slow Soft Shoe

LIT-TLE TIN BOX   A LIT-TLE TIN BOX that a lit - tle tin key un-

97

Promises Promises

Music by Burt Bacharach
Lyrics by Hal David

I'll Never Fall In Love Again

Words by Hal David
Music by Burt Bacharach

All Good Gifts

Words & Music by Stephen Schwartz

Save The People

Words & Music by Stephen Schwartz

Day By Day

Words & Music by Stephen Schwartz

Stranger In Paradise

Words & Music by Robert Wright & George Forrest

Big Spender

Words by Dorothy Fields
Music by Cy Coleman

© Copyright 1965 by Dorothy Fields and Cy Coleman.
Rights assigned to Notable Music Company Incorporated in co-publication with Lida Enterprises Incorporated.
Campbell Connelly & Company Limited, 8/9 Frith Street, London W1.
All Rights Reserved. International Copyright Secured.

I don't pop my cork for ev – 'ry guy I see.___

Hey! Big Spend – er,___ spend a lit – tle time___ with

me. Would – n't you like to have

fun, fun, fun? How's a – bout a few laughs, laughs? I can show you a

good time,___ Let me show you a good time.___ The min-ute you

D. S. al Coda 𝄋

Coda ⊕ Tacet E♭m Tacet Dm

Hey, Big Spend - er!__ Hey, Big Spend - er!__

B♭9 A9 Dm

Spend_____ a lit-tle time_ with me, Spend a lit-tle time_ with

me, Spend a lit-tle time_ with me._____

If My Friends Could See Me Now

Words by Dorothy Fields
Music by Cy Coleman

Sweet Charity

Words by Dorothy Fields
Music by Cy Coleman

Raindrops Keep Falling On My Head

Words by Hal David
Music by Burt Bacharach

I said I did-n't like the way he got things done. Sleep-in' on the job. Those

rain - drops are fall- in' on my head. They keep fall-in'! But there's one thing I know,—

— The blues—— they send—— to meet—— me won't de - feat——

— me. It won't be long—— till hap-pi-ness—— steps up——

The Windmills Of Your Mind

Words by Alan & Marilyn Bergman
Music by Michel Legrand

The Candy Man

Words & Music by Leslie Bricusse & Anthony Newley

Who can take to-mor - row, ___

dip it in a dream, ___ sep - a-rate the sor - row and col-

lect up all the cream? The can-dy man. ___ (The can-dy man, the can-dy man can. ___ the

___ can - dy man can.) The can-dy man can 'cause he mix - es it with love and makes the

Pennies From Heaven

Words by John Burke
Music by Arthur Johnston

The Entertainer

By Scott Joplin

Little Girl

Words & Music by Madeline Hyde & Francis Henry

Nobody Does It Better

Words by Carole Bayer Sager
Music by Marvin Hamlisch

but some-how you found_ me.___ I tried to hide_ from your love light,
when-ev-er you hold_ me.___ There's some kind of mag-ic in-side you

But like heav-en a-bove_ me___ the spy who loved_ me___ is
That keeps me from run-nin'___ but just keep it com-in'___

keep-in' all my se-crets safe to-night.
how'd you learn to do the things you do? do? And

My Own True Love (Tara's Theme)

Words by Mack David
Music by Max Steiner

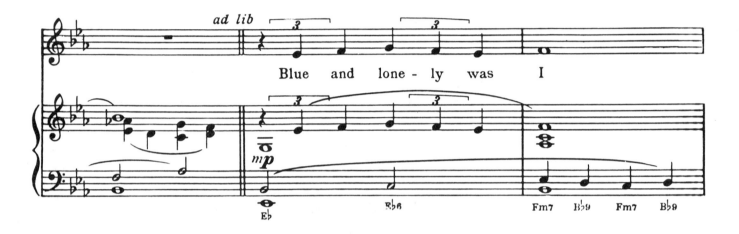

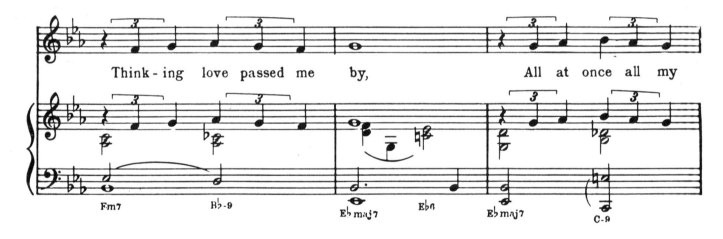

MY OWN TRUE LOVE,   MY OWN TRUE LOVE,

At last I've found you,   MY OWN TRUE LOVE   No lips but

yours,   No arms but yours,   Will ev - er lead me